SOMETHING ROTTEN

"The serpent that did sting thy father's life
Now wears his crown."

Hamlet, Act 1 Scene 5

Titles in Dark Reads:

Badger Publishing Limited, Oldmedow Road, Hardwick Industrial Estate, King's Lynn PE30 4JJ
Telephone: 01438 791037

www.badgerlearning.co.uk

TIM COLLINS

Illustrated by Mark Penman

Something Rotten ISBN 978-1-78464-443-7

Text © Tim Collins 2016
Complete work © Badger Publishing Limited 2016

Publisher: Susan Ross
Senior Editor: Danny Pearson
Editorial Coordinator: Claire Morgan
Copyeditor: Cheryl Lanyon
Designer: Bigtop Design Ltd
Illustrator: Mark Penman

2 4 6 8 10 9 7 5 3 1

SOMETHING ROTTEN

Contents

CHAPTER 1
THE GRAVE

I'm Sam. Six months ago, my dad died.

Three months ago, he started tagging himself in my Facebook photos.

Every time I looked at my phone I'd see Dad tagged in a photo of a family barbeque or seaside trip – always with my mum and my uncle Claude.

At first, I thought someone had hacked into his account.

I messaged the hacker, telling them to stop, but they took no notice.

I tried to ignore it.

I told myself it was just some loser playing a sick joke.

But then they tagged a photo of Dad's grave and it really got to me.

CHAPTER 2
POISON

I shut down Dad's Facebook account, but the hacker set up a new one and kept on tagging him.

He even tagged Dad in a picture he wasn't in. It was taken at Mum's wedding, just two months after Dad's heart attack.

SAMUEL LETT

When Mum got married, I couldn't believe she was ready for a big celebration so soon after Dad's death.

I know I wasn't.

But it was worse than that. She married Dad's brother Claude.

I'd always hated Uncle Claude. And now I had to see him every day.

He slept in Dad's bed, sat in Dad's chair and lived off Dad's savings.

I looked at the wedding picture again. Dad had been tagged in the dark gap between Mum and Uncle Claude.

I started to imagine I could make out a face in the black space.

But it was nothing. Just a shadow.

SAMUEL LETT

The hacker began uploading pictures of their own. They showed a gloomy building with stone arches.

I recognised it as the church where Mum had married Uncle Claude.

The hacker posted pictures from there day and night, as if they were trapped inside.

It seemed like a lot of effort just to wind me up.

I noticed a small brown bottle on the altar of the church. One day, the hacker posted a close-up and I saw it was a type of poison.

I wondered if the hacker was threatening me somehow.

I decided to go to the church and find out.

CHAPTER 3
THE CHURCH

I pushed open the heavy wooden door.

There was a low muttering coming from somewhere in the church.

Through the dim light of the stained-glass windows I could see the bottle of poison on the altar.

I walked down the aisle, sure that someone was about to leap out of the shadows at me.

My phone buzzed and I took it out of my pocket. The hacker had uploaded a new photo.

It showed me opening the church door.

It had been taken just seconds ago. Whoever had posted it was still in there with me!

I crept up to the altar and peered into the gloom beyond. There was no one there.

The whole place was empty, but I could still hear muttering. I recognised my dad's voice.

I heard a scraping noise and saw the bottle of poison moving across the stone surface of the altar.

And that's when I understood what I had to do.

CHAPTER 4
REVENGE

I poured the wine into the glass. Then I added the poison.

I'd spent so long wondering why someone was pretending to be Dad, I'd missed the truth.

It really was him.

He hadn't died of a heart attack. He'd been murdered.

The photos and the poison were his way of telling me what had happened and how I had to get revenge.

I walked into the living room.

Uncle Claude was sitting at the dining table, next to Mum.

I handed the glass of wine to him and watched him drink.

STORY FACTS

This story was inspired by William Shakespeare's *Hamlet*, which is one of the most popular plays in history.

Hamlet is Shakespeare's longest play and takes between four and five hours to perform in full.

Hamlet has influenced many plays, films and novels since it was first performed over 400 years ago. A recent example is Disney's *The Lion King*.

A real human skull was used as a prop in a 2009 production of Hamlet starring David Tennant. A composer left his skull to the Royal Shakespeare Company to be used after his death.

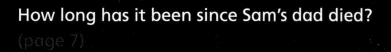

QUESTIONS

How long has it been since Sam's dad died?
(page 7)

Who does Sam's mum marry after his
dad dies?
(page 12)

What is in the bottle at the church?
(page 18)

Where does the muttering come from?
(page 24)

What drink does Sam mix with the poison?
(page 26)

Tim Collins has written over 50 books for children and adults, including *Wimpy Vampire*, *Cosmic Colin*, *Monstrous Maud* and *Dorkius Maximus*. His other teenage fiction for Badger Learning includes *The Black-Eyed Girl*, *Joke Shop* and *Mr Perfect*. Tim has won awards in the UK and Germany.

MEET THE ARTIST

Mark Penman thinks he maybe played one too many fantasy games on his computer. Now it seems he can only silence the horrifying voices in his head by drawing scary stories starring terrified teens.